BRIDGES®
IN MATHEMATICS

SECOND EDITION
STUDENT BOOK

GRADE
K

Published by The MATH LEARNING CENTER Salem, Oregon

Bridges in Mathematics Second Edition Kindergarten Student Book

The Bridges in Mathematics Kindergarten package consists of:

Bridges in Mathematics Kindergarten Teachers Guide Units 1–8

Bridges in Mathematics Kindergarten Assessment Guide

Bridges in Mathematics Kindergarten Teacher Masters

Bridges in Mathematics Kindergarten Student Book

Bridges in Mathematics Kindergarten Home Connections Volumes 1 & 2

Bridges in Mathematics Kindergarten Teacher Masters Answer Key

Bridges in Mathematics Kindergarten Student Book Answer Key

Bridges in Mathematics Kindergarten Home Connections Answer Key

Bridges in Mathematics Kindergarten Components & Manipulatives

Bridges Educator Site

Work Place Games & Activities

Number Corner Kindergarten Teachers Guide Volumes 1–3

Number Corner Kindergarten Teacher Masters

Number Corner Kindergarten Student Book

Number Corner Kindergarten Teacher Masters Answer Key

Number Corner Kindergarten Student Book Answer Key

Number Corner Kindergarten Components & Manipulatives

Word Resource Cards

Digital resources noted in italics.

The Math Learning Center, PO Box 12929, Salem, Oregon 97309. Tel 1 (800) 575-8130
www.mathlearningcenter.org

Prepared for publication using Mac OS X and Adobe Creative Suite.
Printed in the United States of America.

To reorder this book, refer to number 2B0SB5 (package of 5).

QBB0901
05122022_LSB
Updated 2013-10-10.

Bridges in Mathematics is a standards-based K–5 curriculum that provides a unique blend of concept development and skills practice in the context of problem solving. It incorporates Number Corner, a collection of daily skill-building activities for students.

The Math Learning Center is a nonprofit organization serving the education community. Our mission is to inspire and enable individuals to discover and develop their mathematical confidence and ability. We offer innovative and standards-based professional development, curriculum, materials, and resources to support learning and teaching. To find out more, visit us at www.mathlearningcenter.org.

ISBN 978-1-60262-308-8

Bridges Kindergarten
Student Book

The Bridges in Mathematics Kindergarten Student Book is introduced in Unit 6.

Unit 6
Three-Dimensional Shapes & Numbers Beyond Ten

Unit 7
Weight & Place Value

Unit 8
Computing & Measuring with Frogs & Bugs

NAME _____ |**DATE** _____

 Shape Sort & Count

The sorting rule is straight sides and curved sides.
Circle the objects that have only straight sides and
put an X on the objects that have only curved sides.

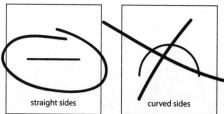

straight sides   curved sides

How many objects with straight sides?

straight sides _____

How many objects with curved sides?

curved sides _____

Use > or < to show which is more or which is less.

How Many Spheres? page 1 of 2

_____

_____

$4 + 2 =$ _____

(continued on next page)

NAME | DATE

How Many Spheres? page 2 of 2

Cut apart the boxes.

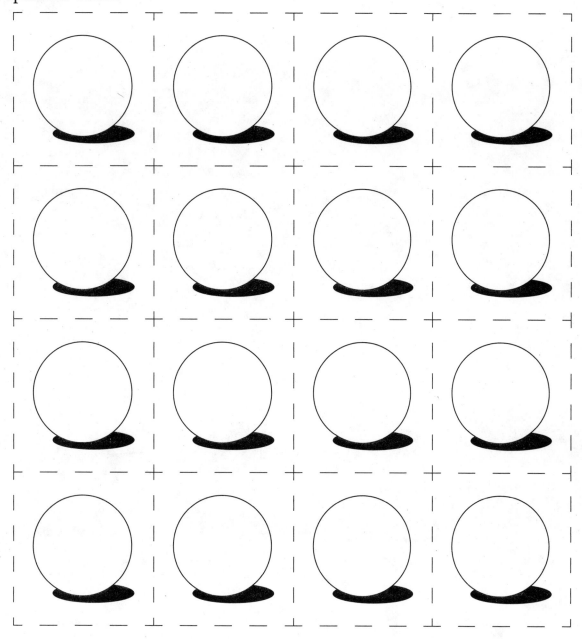

Bingo Shapes page 1 of 2

The bingo shape is a …

The bingo shape is a …

The bingo shape is a …

The bingo shape is a …

The bingo shape is a …

The bingo shape is a …

(continued on next page)

Bingo Shapes page 2 of 2

The bingo shape is a …	The bingo shape is a …
The bingo shape is a …	The bingo shape is a …
The bingo shape is a …	The bingo shape is a …

What's My Rule?

What's My Rule?

What's My Rule?

What's My Rule?

Mystery Numbers page 1 of 2

My Numbers 10–20

(continued on next page)

Mystery Numbers page 2 of 2

My Numbers 10–20

NAME _____ | DATE _____

🔍 A Dime & Some Pennies Record Sheet

11	12	13	14	15	16
11	12	13	14	15	16
11	12	13	14	15	16
11	12	13	14	15	16
11	12	13	14	15	16
11	**12**	**13**	**14**	**15**	**16**

NAME

DATE

Shake Those Beans Five Record Sheet

0+5	1+4	2+3	3+2	4+1	5+0

NAME _____ | **DATE** _____

 ## Sorting Add & Subtract

NAME

DATE

A Pound of Potatoes page 1 of 2

How many objects are in each part of the graph? Write the numbers on this graph. Then draw a picture of the potatoes in the center, one object that is heavier than the potatoes in the *Heavier Than 1 Pound* section, and one object that is lighter than the potatoes in the *Lighter Than 1 Pound* section.

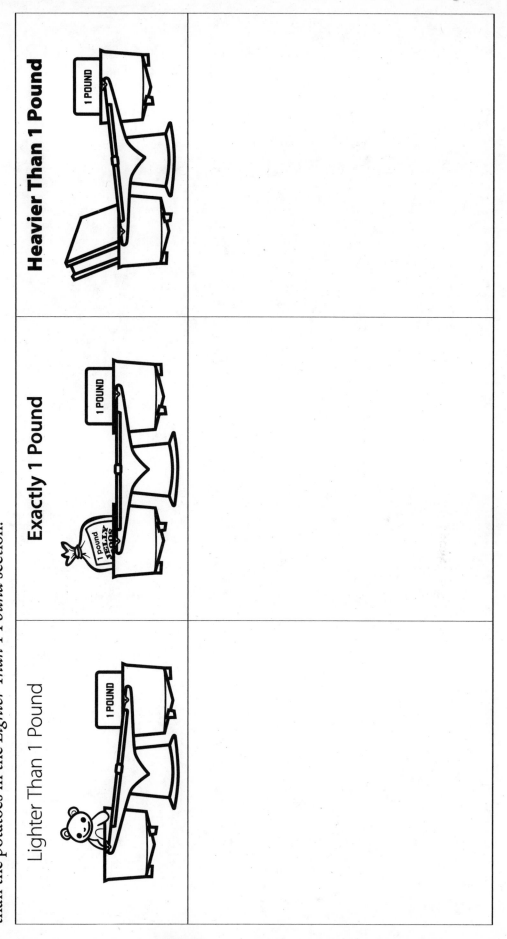

Lighter Than 1 Pound

Exactly 1 Pound

Heavier Than 1 Pound

NAME

DATE

A Pound of Potatoes page 2 of 2

Look at the two objects in each box. Circle the one that you think is *heavier*.

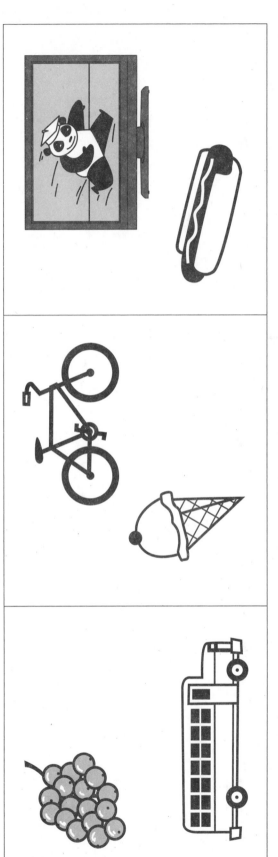

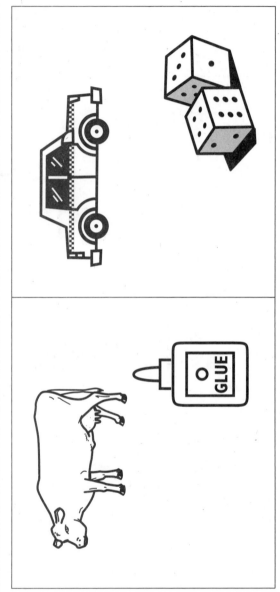

14

Measuring Handfuls

How many Unifix cubes in my handful?

My estimate _____

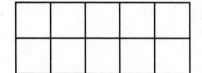  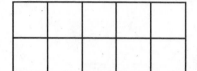

The actual number _____

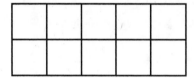  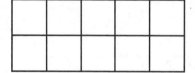

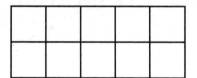

How many Unifix cubes in _____'s handful?

My estimate _____

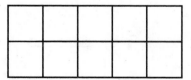 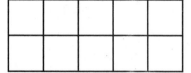 

The actual number _____

 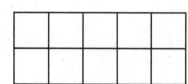

15

🔍 How Many to Make Five?

1 Count the cubes in each group. How many more would it take to make 5? Write the number.

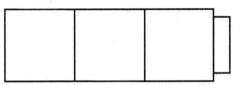   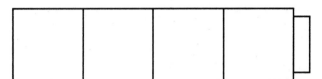

_____   _____

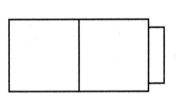   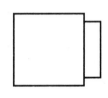

_____   _____

2 Count the cubes. How many more to make 5? Write an equation on the line to show how many cubes in all.

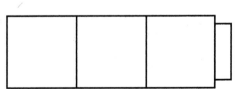   _____ + _____ = _____

NAME _____ DATE _____

Capture the Number, Ten to Twenty

10 11 12 13 14 15 16 17 18 19 20

1 Write the numbers your team captured. _____

2 How many numbers did your team capture? _____

3 How many numbers did the other team capture? _____

4 Write a statement to show which number is greater and which is less.

_____

NAME

DATE

Capture the Number, Zero to Twenty

0 1 2 3 4 5 6 7 8 9 10 11 12 13 14 15 16 17 18 19 20

1 Write the numbers your team captured. _____

2 How many numbers did your team capture? _____

3 How many numbers did the other team capture? _____

4 Write a statement to show which number is greater and which is less.

NAME | DATE

 Story Problems, Part 1 page 1 of 2

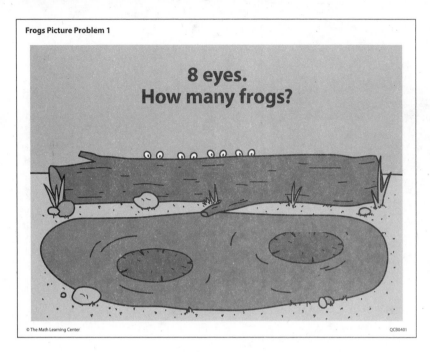

Frogs Picture Problem 1

8 eyes.
How many frogs?

© The Math Learning Center   QCB0401

Story Problems, Part 1 page 2 of 2

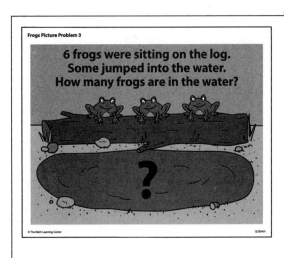

Story Problems, Part 2 page 1 of 2

Frogs Picture Problem 4

3 frogs on the log. 5 frogs in the water. How many more frogs are in the water than on the log?

© The Math Learning Center

QCB0401

NAME | DATE

Story Problems, Part 2 page 2 of 2

Frogs Picture Problem 5

6 frogs.
How many eyes in all?

© The Math Learning Center

QCB0401

Story Problems, Part 3 page 1 of 2

First there are 3 students working in their Student Books, then 2 more students come to join them. How many legs are there in all?

There are 3 chickens are in the barn. How many legs are there in all?

Story Problems, Part 3 page 2 of 2

There are 3 sheep in the barn. How many legs are there in all?

There are 7 animals in the barn. The animals are chickens and sheep. How many legs could there be in all?

Counting Sticks Record Sheet

1 Grab a handful of craft sticks.

2 Estimate the number of sticks you have in your hand.
Write your estimate on the chart below.

3 Organize the sticks into 10s and 1s.

4 Count the actual number of sticks you grabbed.
Write the actual number of sticks on the chart below.

5 Circle the number that represents *more* sticks.

Counting Sticks	
Estimate	**Actual Number of Sticks**

6 **CHALLENGE** For each circled number, work out how many more sticks there are.

Hundreds Chart

1	2	3	4	5	6	7	8	9	10
11	12	13	14	15	16	17	18	19	20
21	22	23	24	25	26	27	28	29	30
31	32	33	34	35	36	37	38	39	40
41	42	43	44	45	46	47	48	49	50
51	52	53	54	55	56	57	58	59	60
61	62	63	64	65	66	67	68	69	70
71	72	73	74	75	76	77	78	79	80
81	82	83	84	85	86	87	88	89	90
91	92	93	94	95	96	97	98	99	100

NAME | **DATE**

 ## Bug Catcher Drawings

Draw a picture to show what happened in the subtraction story. Write an equation underneath your picture.

Bug Catcher Problem 1

Bug Catcher Problem 2

8A Bug Catchers Record Sheet

0   1   2   3   4   5   6   7   8   9   10

8B Piggy Bank Subtraction Record Sheet

0 1 2 3 4 5 6 7 8 9 10

☐ — 🐷 = ☐

31

NAME

DATE

Counting by Twos Mystery Numbers

1	2	3	4	5	6	7	8	9	10
11	12	13	14	15	16	17	18	19	20

Make It Ten Record Sheet

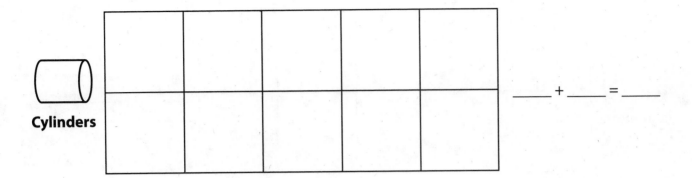

Cylinders

_____ + _____ = _____

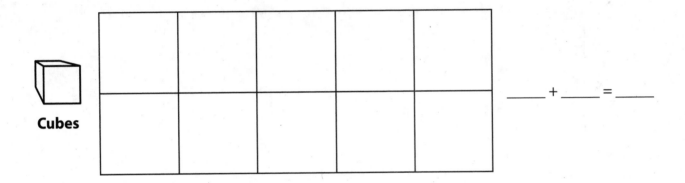

Cubes

_____ + _____ = _____

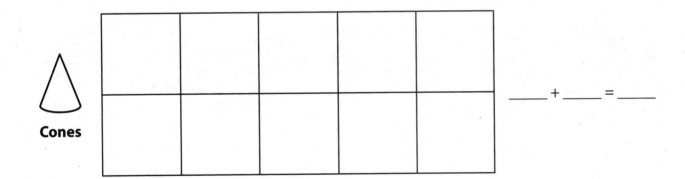

Cones

_____ + _____ = _____

Make It Ten Record Sheet

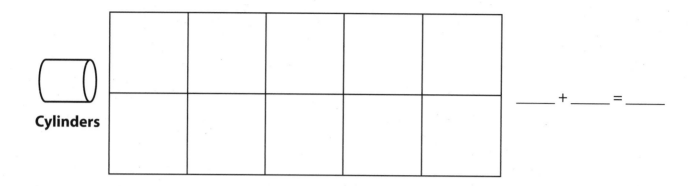

Cylinders

_____ + _____ = _____

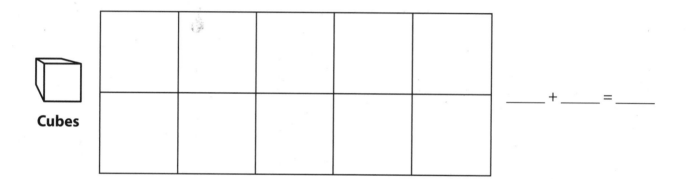

Cubes

_____ + _____ = _____

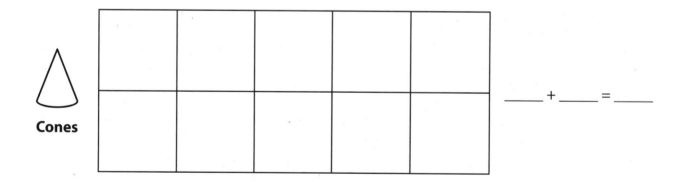

Cones

_____ + _____ = _____

Place Value Mat page 1 of 2

Use cubes to build each number. Once you have built a number, put groups of 10 in the Tens column and single cubes in the Ones column.

Place Value	
Tens	**Ones**

(continued on next page)

NAME | DATE

Place Value Mat page 2 of 2

Write statements to show which number is greater than or less than the other. For example, if one player's number is 14 and the other's is 18, you would write 14 < 18.

Where Do You See It? page 1 of 2

1 Write equations for the ten-frames and circle how you see the equation.

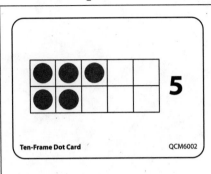

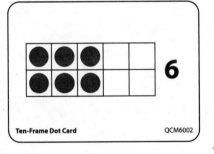

(continued on next page)

Where Do You See It? page 2 of 2

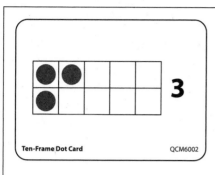

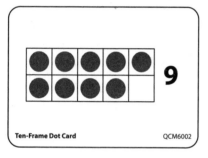

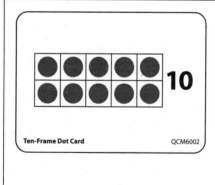

Fact Families page 1 of 2

1 Write the fact family for each five-frame.

39

NAME _____ |**DATE** _____

Fact Families page 2 of 2

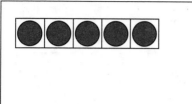

2 Circle the fact family equations that match this five-frame.

$5 - 3 = 2$

$2 + 3 = 5$

$3 + 2 = 5$

$5 - 1 = 4$

$5 - 0 = 5$

$4 + 1 = 5$ $5 - 2 = 3$